‘A down-to-earth guide on how to choose a residential or nursing home.’ *The Guardian*

‘For the first time, a new guide gives invaluable advice on the vexed question of finding a care home . . . Chock full of useful information.’ *The Guardian*

‘*Home from Home* provides the crucial, but dispassionate and practical questions that anyone trying to find a way through the care home maze should ask.’ *Daily Telegraph*

‘If you’re making the choice for someone else, put yourself in their shoes and ask yourself what you would like in a home from home. This book is an excellent guide to doing just that.’ *Daily Telegraph*

‘The King’s Fund guide takes the consumer through the basic steps required to choose a home and gives a comprehensive list of questions to ask and things to look for.’ *The Times*

‘The publication of the new guide, comes at a critical time for the care home industry.’ *The Times*

Home from Home

Your guide to choosing a care home

Edited by Alison Turnbull

Published by
King's Fund Publishing
11–13 Cavendish Square
London W1M 0AN

© King's Fund 1998

First published 1998
Reprinted 1999

ISBN 1 85717 217 5

A CIP catalogue record for this book is available from the British Library

Available from:

King's Fund Bookshop
11–13 Cavendish Square
London W1M 0AN

Tel: 0171 307 2591

Printed and bound in Great Britain

Cover illustration by Minuche Mazumdar Farrar

Contents

Checklists

Acknowledgements

Our thanks to Tessa Brooks, Karen Wright, Tracey Sparkes, Velda Hines, Marcia Kelson, Eileen Shepherd and all the workshop participants.

Original material written by Linda Jarrett.

Edited by Alison Turnbull.

The PPP healthcare group provides health care services to three million people in the UK and overseas. It offers insurance-based schemes which help customers gain access to private medical care at a time of their choosing. The group is also the leading provider of long-term care insurance plans which provide protection against the financial consequences of needing long-term care.

Sponsored by:

Foreword

No one who has ever tried to choose a care home will fail to be moved by this practical, sensible and compassionate guide. For it is immensely difficult. It is difficult to know what to look for, how to check standards are high, how to judge kindness and sensitivity, how to know whether enough nursing support will be offered. Equally, it is hard to understand how the system works, who funds what, what an older person is entitled to, and why there are sometimes problems with discharge from hospital.

Through all this, the person doing the choosing is often not the person who is going to live in the care home. One is choosing for someone else – often for someone vulnerable, possibly confused, and perhaps when a crisis has occurred that makes living at home no longer viable. The sense of responsibility is considerable, and the difficulties may be substantial. So this guide, in simple language, will help in the selection process.

But there is more to it than simple advice. For this guide is based on detailed work surveying care homes over a number of years. This is advice borne of experience, advice that emerges from dispassionate surveying by people who are expert, who know what to look for and know what matters.

I very much hope this guide will become indispensable for people trying to choose a care home, because the messages within it are clear and simple, and the questions to ask are the ones that will enable the questioners to get a good feel for whether the care home will provide tender loving care and professional support. This is a practical guide for people engaged on a difficult quest, and I do believe it will prove helpful and supportive in the process.

Rabbi Julia Neuberger
Chief Executive of the King's Fund

Introduction

The 30,900 residential and nursing homes in the United Kingdom are regulated by government agencies. In recent years King's Fund Organisational Audit (now The Health Quality Service) and other organisations have developed standards for these agencies to use when inspecting homes, and for proprietors to help improve quality. It is a difficult job for professionals to do well – how much harder it must be for those who know nothing about nursing and residential care, nor about the particular needs of older people.

As with every other service you buy – either privately or through the Government – improvements are only likely to be made when consumers are well informed and have the confidence to demand high standards.

This guide has been written with help from people who have had to find a home either for themselves or for a relative or friend and has been developed to help you – the users and purchasers of nursing and residential care – to choose a nursing or residential care home and demand the highest standards of service. It tackles the questions you want and need to ask before choosing the right home either for yourself or for a relative or friend.

There may be many homes to choose from in your area. If you are lucky, choosing the right one will be a gradual process in which you can think carefully about your decision. You may have time to ask for information and support from professionals and specialist organisations.

Sometimes things may need to be organised at great speed, especially if the person needing nursing or residential care is in hospital after experiencing a stroke, accident or illness that prevents them from living at home again. There are so many things to do – sorting out finances, selecting and visiting homes and making a decision about which one to choose.

Even after you have made a decision about what care is appropriate for you, you need to make sure the home chosen continues to provide a high standard of care.

Throughout the guide, we refer to the elderly person as 'she' and 'her' simply because there are many more elderly women in nursing and residential care than men. But all the information here applies equally to men needing nursing or residential care.

A residential home or a nursing home – what's the difference?

Residential homes provide meals and personal care, including help with washing, dressing, getting up and going to bed. Many residential homes provide some nursing care and are required by law to have a qualified nurse on duty. Where the nursing care provided is equivalent to what might be provided by a competent and caring relative, it may not be necessary for a qualified nurse to always be on duty.

Nursing homes provide personal care **and** specialist nursing care (see *Will I need nursing care?* page 45) They must employ qualified nurses and have at least one on duty at all times.

Dual-registered homes are run as combined nursing and residential homes and they are required by law to employ qualified nurses.

We have used the term 'care home' or simply 'home' in this guide to cover all types of home – and we only use 'nursing home' or 'residential home' if it is important to make the distinction between them.

How much does care cost – and who pays?

The average cost of nursing home care is £340 per week, with residential care approximately £250 per week.[1]

You will be asked for details about your **income** and **capital**. This is called a **financial assessment** or **means test** and works out what social services will pay towards the care, and what you will have to pay.

Income = all regular payments to you, such as: pension + benefits + dividends

Capital = your savings + investments + the value of any property you own

Both income and capital are taken into account, but as a general guide, if your total capital[1] is:

Less than £10,000: you will receive some help from the local authority, who will pay the balance of care costs due – up to the

1. June 1998 figures

maximum amount they set – after you have contributed all of your own income. You will be allowed to keep for yourself just the personal expense allowance of less than £15 a week.

It is worth remembering that under the current rules you are not allowed to use up your capital to buy a place in a more expensive home than the local authority maximum allows.

Between £10,000 and £16,000: you will have to contribute to care home fees. Social services use the financial assessment (see Checklist 1, pages 6–7) to work out how much this will be.

More than £16,000: you will probably have to pay the full cost of the care home – and you will have to make the arrangements – until your total capital falls below £16,000. After that time, social services will help, as long as they approve of the home you have chosen.

More than £20,000: you may want to ask an independent financial adviser about the long-term management of your finances.

When you visit a home, ask about the arrangements for payment and what the fees include.

Checklist 1: financial assessment

If social services are contributing to the cost of care:

- ❏   Has the financial assessment been done?

- ❏   Do you know:
    - how much social services will pay? £_____
    - how much you will be expected to pay? £_____

- ❏   Which homes charge within this limit?

- ❏   Are the homes you are planning to visit approved by social services?

If you are paying for your own care:

- ❏   Has your financial situation been reviewed?

- ❏   Will you make payments directly to the home or to social services?

- ❏   If to the home, will you pay:
    - weekly or monthly?
    - in advance or in arrears?

- ❏   What proportion of fees is payable in advance?

- ❏   How often are the fees reviewed?

- ❏   How often are the fees increased?

Checklist 1: financial assessment

❏ What will happen if you cannot afford to keep up the payments?

❏ Which of the following are included in the fees:
- newspapers
- laundry
- hairdressing
- chiropody
- incontinence pads (if needed)
- sheets
- toiletries?

❏ If you go away on holiday, are the fees still payable in full or is a reduction possible?

Who organises care?

The National Health Service

If you are living at home, the NHS professionals that you are most likely to see are your family doctor or your community nurse.

If you are in hospital and are looking for a care home before you can be discharged, there will probably be doctors, nurses, physiotherapists and occupational therapists concerned with your care. They should be involved in your **discharge planning**, and will decide whether you need **continuing care**.

Continuing care, sometimes called **long-term care,** is specialist care provided and paid for by the NHS, either in hospital or a nursing home. Most people discharged from hospital or living at home do not need this type of care.

Discharge planning makes sure that there is a smooth move from hospital to home. It may involve staff from the hospital, the community and social services.

Local authority social services departments

Local authorities arrange **community care** and pay for it for those who need financial help. The **social services department** of the local authority usually assesses what help and support you need.

Community care is provided outside hospitals, in one's own home or in a residential care home. For older people, community care is social or nursing care rather than specialist medical care.

The local authority is the council or borough to which you pay your council tax or rates.

The social services department is not the same as the Department of Social Security (DSS), which runs the Benefits Agency and deals with Income Support and the State Retirement Pension.

Can I organise the care myself?

You do not have to involve social services if you are arranging everything yourself and are paying for the full cost of a care home. However, we suggest that you do contact a care manager – if, in the future, the money to pay for the care home runs out, social services may only be able to help if they originally made an assessment and agreed that a care home was the right option.

Can I look for a home in another area?

Yes. Every local authority can give you a list of homes in their area. However, they are unlikely to arrange visits to the home or give you inspection reports and you will have to organise these things yourself if you are looking for a home outside your local authority.

If you will be receiving financial help from social services, you must make sure that another local authority will pay. The new authority is more likely to do so if you are moving to another area so that you can be nearer to members of your family or friends.

Social services must have a contract with the home – that is an agreement about the level of care and the fees – and this still applies if the home is outside the local authority area.

Who does what?

Care managers work out what kind of care is needed, and arrange care for people who need it.

To contact a care manager, ring the social services department of your local authority (you'll find their number in the local phone book). Explain that you need to move to a care home and that you need a care assessment (see *What is a care assessment?* page 14).

The care manager will also:

- give you written information about what the social services department can do to help

- tell you about discharge arrangements if you are in hospital

- find out how easy it will be for your family and friends to visit you – for example, if you need to be in a home close by because transport is a problem

- give you a copy of the care plan

- give you information about the homes in your chosen area

- show you the inspection reports of homes in your chosen area.

Registered nurses. There must always be a registered nurse on duty in a nursing home, even at night. A registered nurse is responsible for making nursing assessments and for developing care plans, as well as for making sure that the care plan is followed.

Care assistants will provide most of the daily care recommended in the plan.

In residential homes there may not always be a nurse available to make assessments and develop care plans. Care assistants should develop plans for personal care in residential homes – these are usually not as detailed as care plans used in nursing homes.

Key person. You should have a key person who is your main contact and who is responsible for ensuring that you receive the care recommended in the care plan. A key person may be a registered nurse or a care assistant, depending on the level of care needed.

What is a care assessment?

A **care assessment**, sometimes called **needs assessment**, helps the care manager to decide what social, nursing and medical care a person needs.

If you are in hospital, your care manager should carry out the care assessment with hospital staff. The care manager will organise a **case conference** with these people to discuss your needs.

A case conference is a meeting of all the professionals involved in someone's care, to which carers should be asked to contribute, either by attending the meeting or expressing views which the care manager then makes known at the meeting.

If you are at home the care manager may ask for information from your family doctor, district nurse or other health service staff who care for you.

It will be easier to get answers to the more difficult questions if you are closely involved in the assessment processes. You should be able to see copies of the assessment and care plan.

Checklist 2: care assessment – some questions you may be asked

❑   How is your general physical health?

❑   Do you have any specific health problems, such as high blood pressure or diabetes?

❑   How is your mental health?

❑   Do you suffer from memory loss or depression?

❑   Where do you live now?

❑   What social support do you receive?

❑   Do you take part in any social activities?

❑   How well can you:

    – get around indoors?
    – wash?
    – dress?
    – eat meals?
    – get on and off the toilet without help?
    – control your bladder and bowel movements?

❑   What pills and tablets are you taking now?

continued on page 16

Checklist 2: care assessment – some questions you may be asked

❑ Do you need special nursing care, for example with:

  – continence?

  – pressure sores?

  – leg ulcers?

❑ How do you want to be cared for?

What is a care plan?

The care manager uses all the information in the assessment to decide on the **care plan.**

A **care plan** is a written description of the level of care someone needs and can expect to receive. A complete care plan should include a goal for everything that is being assessed.

The home you choose should receive a copy of this assessment, but you would expect staff at a good home to carry out their own assessment and then to plan the care they will provide. A **nursing and residential care plan** (see Checklist 3 on pages 19–20) should:

- be regularly reviewed
- include information about the type of home and the level of care that will be suitable
- take account of a resident's changing health and social needs
- describe how the resident is expected to maintain certain abilities and activities
- describe targets for improvement, where appropriate
- include details of the resident's preferences and views.

Each resident will have a different care plan. The assessment leading to the plan will be more detailed than the one carried out by social services, although the same points are included.

Checklist 3: what's in a full nursing or residential care plan?

❑ Personal details – date of birth, relatives, next of kin, telephone numbers

❑ Social information – previous places lived, work, family, interests

❑ Preferences about daily life – for example getting up late, bathing once a week

❑ Food preferences and any dietary needs

❑ The part relatives and friends wish to play

❑ General health record, including past medical history

❑ Risk assessment* for safety

❑ The extent of confusion or challenging behaviour

❑ Risk assessment for manual handling

❑ Risk assessment for pressure sores

❑ Medications and treatment

❑ Nursing care requirements

❑ How well you are able to care for yourself

continued on page 20

---

* Older people who are dependent are said to be 'at risk' from certain events. For example, a resident who is immobile and spends long periods of time in bed or in the same position in a chair may be at risk of developing a pressure sore.

Checklist 3: what's in a full nursing or residential care plan?

❑ The help you need and your preferences for how help should be given

❑ Your preferences about future care options

❑ Religious and cultural background, and associated activities, such as attending religious services

❑ Any expressed wishes about death and dying

Checklist 4: care assessment

❑ Have you received an information leaflet from social services?

❑ Has the care assessment been done?

❑ Have you received a copy of the assessment and care plan?

If you do not understand something in either the assessment or care plan, ask your care manager to explain

How do I find out about care homes?

Care manager

Your care manager may help you to visit homes before you make a choice, unless you are paying in full for your own care and you are making all the arrangements yourself.

Word of mouth

Perhaps you know someone living in a home or someone with a relative in a home who can give you a first-hand account of their experience. This type of information is very valuable.

Telephone

Ring around a number of homes and ask for brochures and leaflets.

Checklist 5: homes in your area

- ❑ Has your care manager given you a list of homes in the area?
- ❑ Do you know which homes are within your budget?
- ❑ Do you want to pay extra to have a wider choice of homes?
- ❑ What will happen if the money runs out in the future?
- ❑ Have you seen the inspection reports of homes you want to visit? If not, ask your care manager how you can get hold of them

Can I talk to someone else who has been through this?

The Relatives Association (details on page 69) may be able to put you in touch with someone locally who is happy with the care their relative is receiving.

Many homes encourage relatives' groups which meet regularly to discuss life in the home and make suggestions for changes and improvements. They may also be involved in fund-raising activities. Such groups usually have a good relationship with home owners and staff, who find them a great help.

Relatives' groups are a good source of information when you are making a decision about a home, and if you have shortlisted one, you could ask to meet the group to find out about their view of life in the home. If there is no such group, you can ask to meet one of the residents or a relative of one of them. You can also ask the home owner or staff how they find out about a relative's opinion.

Checklist 6: relatives' group

❑   Is there a relatives' group already active in the home?

❑   How often and when does it meet?

❑   Does the group keep notes of meetings and decisions?

❑   How has the group been active in the past year?

How do I choose a home?

You will probably want to visit a number of homes before you decide on the right one. Visiting homes takes time, and afterwards you will want to make sense of what you have been told. This will be easier if you plan your visit beforehand, decide what you are looking for and have your questions or checklist organised so that you can make sure you cover everything.

Before asking questions, think about the answer you will be looking for.

> *Example: If you are told that no activities are arranged for residents because the staff prefer to let them do what they want, you may think that this sounds positive and flexible. The consequence might be that all the residents sit around doing nothing.*

Decide which homes you will go to see. This decision will be based on the information the social services department gives you, or other sources of information (see *How do I find about care homes?* page 21).

Make arrangements to visit the home. When you can visit may not be when many of the professional staff are on duty. Telephone homes to make an appointment with a named member of staff – preferably the home owner or manager – and ask if you can meet some of the staff who work in the home when you visit.

Ask to see the inspection report if you are visiting a nursing home or dual-registered home.

Take your time and don't be afraid to ask questions. Staff at a good home will understand that you have concerns and will be more than happy to give you the time to look around, ask questions and then decide.

Be prepared to visit more than once. You will not be able to assess the home fully after only one visit and you will probably have a lot more questions after you leave. If you like a home, try to visit again at a different time of the day and week. You can even call in without making an appointment – the welcome you receive could tell you a lot about the staff's attitude to visitors.

Ask if you can meet different members of staff and relatives of the residents that live there.

If you are choosing a home for a relative or a friend, spend some time 'in their shoes', trying to imagine what they would like. Their tastes and preferences may be different from yours. Ask your relative if you can, or ask someone speaking on their behalf, what they would like out of a home.

Checklist 7: what would you like out of a home?

❑   A room of your own?

❑   Companionship?

❑   The opportunity to keep up current activities?

❑   What do you like best about your present home?

❑   What will you find difficult to give up?

Think about the way you live now. If you like to live with a lot of possessions around, in a house that is a bit of a muddle but full of character, you might be comfortable choosing a home that is not very modern.

If you prefer a very neat and tidy home, you might find that a home with a more 'clinical' feel is more acceptable.

If you have a lot of visitors, you will want to make sure that staff are happy for residents to have visitors, and find out about visiting times.

If you only socialise outside the home in a day centre or church, you will want to know that staff can organise transport for you to continue to visit the day centre and church.

Compromise. It is unlikely that one home will provide everything you hope for, and you may have to decide what it is that you will give up – even something that originally seemed important – because the home has something else that no other home offers.

> *Example: You may have asked for a nice view from your room and a garden where you can work from time to time. You may have a choice between a home with a garden and special programme for residents who want to look after it, but with a room without a view, and a home where all the rooms have a lovely view but a very small garden only suitable for residents to walk in.*

Some of the decisions will be based on practical aspects of providing care and may have nothing to do with what you would prefer in terms of home comfort.

> *Example: If you find that a home has a number of special mattresses to treat people who have pressure sores, you may reject it in favour of the home that has a pressure sore prevention policy, and where all staff are aware of and contribute to care plans that aim to prevent pressure sores appearing in the first place. You may decide to do this even if the second home has no garden at all.*

Weighing up the advantages of different homes and their approach to care will never be easy unless one home stands out above all the others. If you, your friends and other family members take the time to discuss preferences, and why they are important, before visiting homes, the process should be easier.

What questions should I ask when I visit the home?

All the people we talked to about finding a home agreed that it is important to feel confident that the home is taking a real interest in the potential resident. Be wary of homes that immediately respond with 'Yes, we have a room' without asking anything about yourself.

Staff should try to find out about a potential resident before they decide that they can offer a place. If the home does not know about your likes, dislikes, preferences and – possibly – the things that are unique to you as an individual, how can they tell if you will fit in with other residents or if they offer the right type of accommodation and activities?

Examples:
- *You may be the life and soul of the party, or you may like to read quietly for long periods and not be interested in joining in social events.*
- *You may be coming from your own home, where the garden was the most important thing in your life.*
- *You may be devoted to your grandchildren who visit you once a week for tea.*

You should not have to offer this type of information. If a home is going to welcome residents to an environment that aims to stimulate and care, the interest and concern should come from the staff of the home.

Checklist 8: what staff should ask you on your first visit

- ❑ What do you like to be called?
- ❑ What contact will you have with other family members?
- ❑ Who will visit you and how often?
- ❑ Where do you live now?
- ❑ Do you have friends close by?
- ❑ Do you have any special diet or food preferences?
- ❑ How is your general health?
- ❑ Do you have any long-term health problems, such as diabetes or continence?
- ❑ Where have you lived before?
- ❑ Did you work outside the home?
- ❑ What are the important family events?
- ❑ What hobbies, activities or interests do you currently enjoy?

Checklist 8: what staff should ask you on your first visit

❑   Do the staff invite you to:

    – visit at different times?

    – talk to residents?

    – talk to staff?

    – meet relatives of residents?

If not, and you like the home, ask if you can do these things.

❑   *For those choosing a home for a relative or a friend:* Can we visit your relative/friend to make our first assessment? A good home will want to meet the potential resident before agreeing to accept them.

Checklist 9: what to ask staff on your first visit

❑ Do the staff offer a trial period for you to live in the home?

It is probably best to use a trial period only if you feel confident about the home. Moving again may be traumatic.

❑ What is the gender of the other residents?

❑ Do any couples live in the home?

Most residents of care homes are women. If you are male, think about whether you would be happy with no other men around. The male : female ratio may not always be the same.

❑ What is the level of mental awareness of the other residents?

❑ What proportion of residents can carry on conversations?

The answer to this question can change over time.

❑ What does this home do to make sure that residents receive individual care (defined on page 51)?

At the very least you should be told that each resident has an individual care plan and someone responsible for assessment and planning.

Checklist 9: what to ask staff on your first visit

❑ How do the staff ensure that the individual resident's dignity is maintained?

Staff should be able to give you a full answer about what maintaining respect and dignity means to the home and its staff, and how they ensure that all employees understand their commitment to these important rights.

You can use the response you get on this first visit to ask follow-up questions to staff you meet later. This will tell you whether the owner or manager's commitment is reflected by the staff.

❑ If residents have a hearing or visual impairment, what do the staff do to cope with this?

❑ How will the staff know if the problem deteriorates?

❑ What arrangements are there for eye and hearing tests?

❑ If your ethnic background is different from the majority of the other residents you might want to ask questions about:

   – language

   – diet and food preferences

   – religious festivals and customs

   – availability of quiet areas for religious activities.

Checklist 10: what to look out for and think about on your first visit

- ❏ Is there anyone living in the home that you already know?
- ❏ Will the home be convenient for your friends and family members to visit?
- ❏ Is it close to a busy road?
- ❏ Are shops and post office accessible?

- ❏ On entering the home, do you immediately feel welcome?
- ❏ Do the staff greet you or smile at you when they pass?
- ❏ Do the residents generally look happy?
- ❏ Do some of the residents smile at staff or visitors?
- ❏ Are some residents talking to each other, with staff or visitors?
- ❏ Are the residents doing different things or is everyone doing the same thing (or nothing)?

- ❏ Does the home smell clean when you enter?
- ❏ Is the general level of cleanliness acceptable?
- ❏ Are the bathrooms and toilets clean?

Checklist 10: what to look out for and think about on your first visit

❑   Is the standard of decoration acceptable?

❑   Does the brochure or leaflet about the home describe what the home is hoping to achieve and its approach to care?

What facilities should I be looking for?

Checklist 11: facilities in the home

❑ What types of rooms (single, double or shared) are available?

❑ Is your preference possible?

❑ Once a resident has moved in, do they ever have to move to a different room?

❑ Is it possible to have en suite facilities?

❑ If so, is there an extra charge?

❑ How big are the rooms?

❑ When you are shown a room, do staff ask the resident's permission?

Residents should be allowed to deny access to their room to strangers.

❑ Do all the rooms look the same?

If a home offers individual care, residents should be encouraged to make their rooms their own.

Checklist 11: facilities in the home

❑ Can you bring some or all of your own furniture?

Think about what you might want to take with you – will it fit?

❑ Can residents have a television in their room?

❑ Do rooms have telephone sockets?

❑ Is there an extra charge for either of these?

❑ When can relatives and friends visit?

❑ Does the home have overnight facilities for visitors? If so:

  – what are the booking arrangements?

  – is there a charge?

❑ Is there a garden? If so:

  – is it secure for residents to walk or sit in?

  – do residents help with gardening?

  – are there any restrictions on residents' access to the garden?

❑ Is there a choice of menu?

❑ Can relatives stay for meals with residents?

❑ Can relatives prepare meals for residents?

continued on page 40

Checklist 11: facilities in the home

❑ Can alternative arrangements be made if mealtimes are missed due to regular outside activity?

❑ Is smoking allowed in the home?

❑ If so, are there any restrictions?

❑ Is drinking alcohol allowed in the home?

❑ If so, are there any restrictions?

❑ Are residents allowed to own pets or are pets allowed to visit?

❑ What are the laundry arrangements?

❑ How do staff make sure that belongings are returned to the right owner?

❑ Are there any communal items of clothing?

❑ How do staff balance security with the freedom of residents and visitors to have access?

❑ Does the home have its own transport? If so:
   – what is it usually used for during a typical week?
   – who is the driver and what other responsibilities does she or he have?

Checklist 11: facilities in the home

❏ If the home does not have its own transport, how do residents travel?

There are many things homes can do, but if there is no provision for transport, residents may be permanently tied to the home unless a relative or friend comes to take them out.

❏ Does a hairdresser visit the home regularly? If so:

- how often?

- how are appointments made?

- is there an extra charge?

❏ Do all residents go to bed and get up at the same time?

❏ Do all residents have meals together?

All homes have a routine but the readiness to change it to suit a particular resident's needs is a simple indicator of flexibility.

❏ Do residents have access to their rooms at all times?

❏ Does every resident have a space in their room that can be locked and in which they can keep personal belongings?

❏ Do residents manage their own money?

continued on page 42

Checklist 11: facilities in the home

❑ Can residents choose their bathtime?

Some people are used to having a bath or shower every day, or every two days, or once a week. Is the home flexible enough to maintain individual routines?

❑ What happens when a resident is taken ill?

❑ Does a general practitioner (GP) visit regularly?

❑ What are the arrangements for registration with a GP?

Can residents remain registered with their own GP, if she or he is in the area?

❑ How is medication kept under review?

❑ What are the arrangements for administering drugs?

Can residents take responsibility for their own drugs or are they always administered by staff?

❑ Does the home have any arrangements for a physiotherapist to visit the home to treat residents? If so:

– how does this work?

– is there a charge?

Checklist 11: facilities in the home

❏ Does the home have any arrangements for dental care? If so:

 – what are they?

 – how do they work?

❏ Does the home have any arrangements for visits by an optician? If so:

 – how often?

 – how are residents told about the visits?

❏ How do staff know if residents have a foot problem?

❏ Who cuts toenails for residents who are unable to do it for themselves?

❏ Does a chiropodist visit the home? If so:

 – how often?

 – which residents are treated?

 – is there a charge?

❏ Will it be possible for you to carry on visiting day centres or church and to take part in other activities as you do now?

❏ How many other residents are active in this way?

continued on page 44

Checklist 11: facilities in the home

☐ Do religious ministers visit residents?

☐ What regular activities are arranged by the home for the residents?

☐ Who is responsible for making sure they happen?

☐ What arrangements are made for residents who would like to do something different?

☐ Do the staff organise trips or holidays for residents?

☐ When and where was the last trip?

☐ How many residents went on it?

☐ How much do trips cost?

☐ What happens at Christmas, Easter and bank holidays?

☐ Is there an opportunity for residents to enrol in adult education courses? If so:

    – how many residents are involved in such courses?

    – where do they study?

    – what do they study?

Will I need nursing care?

Before choosing a nursing or residential home, make an appointment to see your family doctor or community nurse – they are in a good position to assess your need for nursing care.

As we get older, our bodies do not work so well and some deterioration is inevitable. Some problems arise because changes have gone unnoticed. These problems need specialised nursing care or people suffering from them can deteriorate surprisingly quickly making them more vulnerable to other problems.

> *Example: If an older person catches flu and has to spend some time in bed, she could develop a pressure sore. This can be extremely uncomfortable and could result in a longer period in bed. An older person finds it much more difficult to walk again if she has been off her feet for a long time and, without proper help and support, she may become increasingly immobile – all because of a bout of flu.*

With the right care and attention the progress and severity of the problems can be reduced.

Problems which may require nursing care include:

- mental illness
- poor appetite
- reduced mobility
- incontinence
- skin problems.

Mental illness. This includes depression, confusion, memory loss, anxiety and dementia, such as Alzheimer's disease. People with dementia can be confused and forgetful and not know where they are.

Poor appetite. If older people do not eat well, it can affect their general health. People should be able to eat food they find appetising, but sometimes older people find food less appetising because they:

- have a reduced sense of smell and taste
- find it hard to chew and swallow because they are producing less saliva
- have problems with painful teeth or dentures that do not fit properly
- have indigestion and constipation because they are not moving around very much.

People who have had a stroke may have poor muscle control around the mouth and tongue, and find it particularly difficult to swallow.

Mobility. Some elderly people find it hard to accept that they can't do simple things any more, such as getting in and out of bed, sitting down and walking around their home or garden. It is possible to help people retain mobility if there has been a proper assessment which can identify any of the common problems that restrict mobility, such as pain, arthritis, osteoporosis, Parkinson's disease, stroke and foot problems. Prescribed drugs may sometimes affect a person's mobility.

Incontinence. When people lose control of their bladder or (less commonly) their bowels, there is usually an underlying problem that can be treated. This can only happen if staff take the time to assess the problem and develop a plan to cope with it.

Skin problems. Older people are highly susceptible to skin damage, such as pressure sores, leg ulcers and wounds from cuts, burns or other minor injuries. Staff should understand how pressure sores can be prevented or treated. Prevention is especially important for bed- or chair-bound residents.

Checklist 12: nursing care

Mental illness

❑ Is the care plan based on the individual resident's needs, preferences and activities, and not on a general plan that applies to everyone in the home (or everyone with a mental illness in the home)?

❑ Do residents have access to privacy?

❑ Do they live as independently as possible?

❑ Are residents treated with dignity – and how is this guaranteed if they are unable to speak for themselves?

❑ How are relatives included in making choices about treatment and care?

Nutrition

❑ Does the home provide special diets for residents with religious or cultural food preferences?

❑ Do the staff find out about what a resident likes to eat?

❑ Do staff plan menus with residents?

❑ How often are separate meals prepared for people with special likes or dislikes?

❑ How do the staff know if a resident has difficulty eating?

Checklist 12: nursing care

❏ How many residents need help with eating and drinking?

❏ How do the staff cope?

❏ What happens if a resident is not eating the meals that are prepared for her?

❏ Do the staff keep a record of how often, how well and how much residents eat and drink?

Observation
Visit at mealtimes.
Are any residents left alone, unable to manage to eat their meal?
Ask to see meal plans.

Continence care

❏ What happens if a resident becomes incontinent?

❏ Do the staff try to find out what is causing the problem?

❏ Can the home show you a plan for promoting continence?

❏ How is this personalised?

❏ Do nurses take courses to update their training on continence care?

❏ Is there any contact with a district nurse or continence specialist?

continued on page 50

Checklist 12: nursing care

Observation

Is there a stale smell of urine in the home? A home should not smell of urine even if some residents are incontinent and need care with pads. A smell only arises if residents are left without adequate care.

Mobility

❑ Do care plans assess mobility, even for residents who are extremely immobile?

❑ How do staff encourage residents to keep mobile?

Observation

Are floors slip-resistant?
Are handrails provided everywhere?

Skin care

❑ What is done to prevent pressure sores?

❑ What training do staff have in prevention?

❑ What equipment, such as special mattresses, is available for residents who are likely to get pressure sores?

❑ How do staff keep up to date with skin care?

How can I tell if the care I receive is quality care?

Nursing and personal care that focus on prevention and treatment can promote health and improve residents' well-being. The home and its staff should recognise this and work towards not just providing good care, but improving the quality of life for each person in the home.

Staff should be able to tell you how they will look after a resident *as an individual*. They should establish **individual care** plans which are based on each resident's problem or illness, preferences and activities, not on a general plan that applies to everyone in the home (or everyone with that particular problem in the home).

Individual care is vital. If, when you first visit a home, you find out that everyone in that home always gets the same meal at the same time, or that promoting continence is never an option, or that residents who could get around with some help are left sitting in a chair all day, ask yourself whether this is a home you want to live in.

Individual care is based on the needs of the individual and is only possible if that person has had a thorough assessment of her needs. For example, an individual care plan might say that a resident will have lunch in her room every day because she prefers to eat alone.

How can I make sure my relative or friend is involved in decisions about her own care?

Although your relative or friend is at the centre of all this activity, she may feel left out. You may feel confident to make decisions on her behalf, or you may want to do all you can to include her in the planning and decision making. In any case, you will want to explain what is happening.

If you talk to others in the family about the best way to include your relative or friend you may identify someone who feels particularly able to do this. Or can ask one of the voluntary agencies, such as Age Concern (address on page 67) to put you into contact with someone working as an **advocate**.

An **advocate** is someone acting independently who is skilled in speaking on behalf of vulnerable people who are unable to speak for themselves. An advocate may be able to help you find a way to include your relative or friend in decision making about her care.

What happens when I have chosen the home?

When you have decided on a home you will want to make sure that you, your family members, carers and staff at the home all clearly understand what is being provided. If social services are contributing to the fees, they will have a contract with the home, and if you are paying the full fees for a home, you will have a contract that lays out the financial arrangements. It is becoming more common for residents to have a more detailed contract agreeing the terms and conditions under which they live in the home.

The Continuing Care Conference (CCC) is a group of commercial, charitable and public sector organisations with an interest in continuing care for older people. CCC has drawn up a framework contract (see Checklist 13, page 54) to help residents and care homes agree the terms and conditions of care to be provided by a home.

If the home you choose offers you a contract that it usually uses to agree terms and conditions, you may find it useful to compare its content with that of the CCC. If you feel there is something missing from the contract you are offered, ask for it to be included before you agree and sign the document.

Checklist 13: framework contract for agreeing terms and conditions of care

The contract should include:

- ❑ assessment and care planning
- ❑ what is included in the fees
- ❑ facilities
- ❑ visiting
- ❑ medical arrangements
- ❑ staffing
- ❑ insurance
- ❑ privacy and confidentiality
- ❑ personal money
- ❑ regular reviews
- ❑ complaints procedures
- ❑ temporary absence
- ❑ termination procedure

You can get copies of the framework contract from: The Continuing Care Conference, 12 College Street, London SW1P 3SH.

How can relatives and friends help when I move in?

How the home includes you in decisions about your care and life in the home may be an important deciding factor in your choice of home. One of your relatives or friends may be closely involved in your care – perhaps you live with them at the moment. When you move into your new home, they may want to contribute to your care when they visit you.

> *Example: They may want to help at mealtimes or take you to the toilet. Sometimes there is conflict between visitors and staff in the home who see it as their job to care for residents.*

If you want a relative or a friend to help look after you when they visit, it is worth asking whether it is usual for this to happen. If it is not, talk to the owner and staff about how you would like them to be involved. This way you can make sure that your wishes will be taken into account, and not overlooked.

How can I be sure that the home is well run?

It is important to know that a home is properly and well run.

However well staff believe they are delivering care, in a good home they will always see that there is room for improvement. Staff may be working to standards that are set by the home, a home association or an outside body. Whatever they are doing, it must involve some measurement of care, and they should be able to describe this to you in a way that you can understand.

Checklist 14: how the home is run

❑ Who is in charge of the home?

You should expect this question to be answered without hesitation. Ask about different times of the day and night.

❑ What are the arrangements if the person usually in charge is away from the home?

❑ Is the home a member of an association that promotes good standards in care homes (see pages 65–66)

❑ Is there an induction programme for new staff?

❑ How do new staff find out and how soon do they learn about the way the home cares for residents?

❑ How many trained staff are employed in the home?

❑ What hours do they work?

❑ Does the home use agency staff? If so:

– how often?

– how does the home make sure that agency staff are familiar with the residents and their needs?

continued on page 58

Checklist 14: how the home is run

❑ Who works at night?

Some homes use agency staff because it is difficult to find permanent staff to work at night.

❑ Can the home demonstrate how it values the staff it employs?

The home's attitude to training is important. Also ask about what else the home does to encourage staff to stay with the home.

❑ What is the home doing to improve care?

❑ What training programmes are available to staff?

❑ How many staff have undergone training in the past year?

❑ Ask to see the training plans for care staff.

You would expect to see a clear record of planned and achieved training.

Checklist 14: how the home is run

❏   How do the staff find out about a resident's needs, wishes or opinions if she is unable to speak for herself and does not have a relative or friend who is involved with the home?

The answer to this question may be a good indicator of a home's attitude to the residents it cares for. A home that uses an independent advocate to speak on behalf of residents will probably be doing all it can to ensure that all residents take part in the running of the home.

The Health Quality Service in association with the King's Fund has developed a set of standards covering every aspect of the running of the home. Ask the person who runs the home whether they are aware of and/or use the standards to ensure that they are achieving best practice at all times.

How can I be sure that the home will keep up its standards of care?

Your individual needs must be regularly and routinely assessed. Staff should be able to tell you how often assessments and care plans are reviewed. There should be clear responsibility for assessment and care plans and if nursing care is provided this responsibility should lie with a nurse.

Relatives and friends involved in the care of a resident should make regular appointments with the resident's care manager so that they can keep up to date with what is happening, and with what changes, if any, need to be made. Formal meetings to discuss care are better than informal chats in the hallway.

If you find some of the technical terms baffling, don't be afraid to ask for a simpler explanation. If you think that you are not being told everything, write down a list of questions to ask your care manager. If he or she cannot answer them, arrange to meet again when they have obtained the answers.

Checklist 15: continuing assessment and care planning

❏ How often are a resident's care needs assessed?

❏ Who carries out assessments and decides on care plans?

❏ Are there regular meetings between staff to discuss care plans?

❏ Does each resident have his or her own care plan?

❏ Where is this kept?

❏ Who has access to it?

❏ How are a resident's preferences and needs determined?

❏ When and how are relatives included in assessments?

❏ Where are a resident's preferences noted on the care plan?

Observation
Ask to see a typical care plan. There should be a form that prompts whoever is completing the assessment and plan to write about the abilities and achievements of the resident. Look out for regular updates, and dated and signed entries.

Resources

Your care manager should be able to give you all the information you need, but you can also contact the charities and voluntary organisations whose aim is to offer information and advice for people in your position. Use them – their experience and knowledge are invaluable.

- *Some organisations make a small charge for leaflets and factsheets*
- *Most appreciate a stamped addressed envelope if you are writing*
- *Calls to numbers beginning with 0800 are free*
- *Calls to numbers beginning with 0345, 0845 are billed at local rates*
- *For most helplines the best time to call is between 10am and 4pm, Monday–Friday*

Accommodation

Elderly Accommodation Counsel advises people about retirement housing options, including residential care homes and nursing homes. They have a database that can generate information about homes in a particular area.

Elderly Accommodation Counsel
46a Chiswick High Road
London W4 1SZ
Tel: 0181 742 1182

Financial information and advice

Age Concern Insurance Services
Garrod House
Chaldon Road
Caterham
Surrey CR3 5YZ
Tel: 01883 346964

Association of British Insurers
51 Gresham Street
London EC2V 7HQ
Tel: 0171 600 3333
http://www.abi.org.uk

Benefit Enquiry Line gives information about state benefits and offers help with completing claim forms.
Freefone: 0800 882 200
Textphone (for those hard of hearing): 0800 243 787
http://www.dss.gov.uk/ba

Carersline provides specialist benefits advice for carers.
Tel: 0345 573 369

Independent Financial Advice Bureau can send you a list of independent financial advisers in your area.

Independent Financial Advice Bureau
549 Green Lanes
London N8 0RQ
Tel: 0181 348 4466

Nursing Home Fees Agency provides information on legal and financial matters.

Nursing Home Fees Agency
Old Bank House
95 London Road
Headington
Oxford OX3 9AE
Tel: 01865 750 665

Care home organisations

These are organisations to which care homes can pay a fee to belong. In doing so, they agree to adhere to a code of practice or standards set and monitored by the organisation.

British Federation of Care Home Proprietors
840 Melton Road
Thurmaston
Leicester LE4 8BN
Tel: 0116 264 0095
http://www.martex.co.uk/bfchp

The Health Quality Service
11–13 Cavendish Square
London W1M 0AN
Tel: 0171 307 2400

Independent Healthcare Association
22 Little Russell Street
London WC1A 2HT
Tel: 0171 430 0537

National Care Homes Association
Fourth Floor
45–47 Leather Lane
London EC1N 7TJ

Registered Nursing Homes Association
Calthorpe House
Hagley Road
Edgbaston
Birmingham B16 8QY
Tel: 0121 454 2511
http://www.intercarenet.co.uk

General information and advice

Action on Elder Abuse
Astral House
1268 London Road
London SW16 4ER
Freefone: 0800 731 4141

Age Concern campaigns on behalf of older people and produces factsheets

Age Concern England
Astral House 1268 London Road
London SW16 4ER
0181 679 8000
http://www.ace.org.uk/

Age Concern Northern Ireland
3 Lower Crescent
Belfast BT7 1NR
Tel: 01232 245 729

Age Concern Scotland
113 Rose Street
Edinburgh EH2 3DT
Tel: 0131 220 3345

Age Concern Cymru
Fourth floor
1 Cathedral Road
Cardiff CF1 9SD
Tel: 01222 371 566

Northern Ireland
113 University Street
Belfast BT7 1HP
Tel: 01232 439 843

Scotland
11 Queen's Crescent
Glasgow G1 2LL
Tel: 0141 333 9495

Wales
Pantglas Industrial Estate
Bedwas
Newport NP1 8DR
Tel: 01222 880 176

Community Health Councils (CHCs)
There is a CHC in every health authority which can give you advice about your contact with the Health Service. In particular, the CHC will help you if you want to make a complaint. Look up the number in your local phone book.

Counsel and Care provides information and advice for people over 60, their carers, friends and relatives. The helpline advises callers on welfare benefits, accommodation, community care and hospital discharge.

Counsel and Care
Twyman House
16 Bonny Street
London NW1 9PG
Tel: 0845 300 7585

Help the Aged publishes free advice leaflets and runs a free helpline (Seniorline) for older people, their relatives and friends.

Help the Aged
St James's Walk
Clerkenwell Green
London EC1R 0BE
Freefone: 0800 289 404

Relatives Association advises people living in residential or nursing homes and their relatives and friends.

Relatives Association
5 Tavistock Place
London WC1H 9SN
Tel: 0171 916 6055

Organisations for people with specific health problems or disabilities

Alzheimer's Disease Society
Gordon House
10 Greencoat Place
London SW1P 1PH
Tel: 0845 300 336
http://www.vois.org.uk

Arthritis Care
18 Stephenson Way
London NW1 2HD
Frrefone: 0800 289 170
http://www.vois.org.uk/arthritiscare

Arthritis and Rheumatism Council for Research
PO Box 31
Newark
Notts NG24 2BS

British Diabetic Association
10 Queen Anne Street
London W1M 0BD
Tel: 0171 636 6112
http://www.diabetes.org.uk

CancerBACUP
3 Bath Place
Rivington Street
London EC2A 3JR
Freefone: 0800 181 199
http://www.cancerbacup.org.uk

Continence Foundation
307 Hatton Square
16 Baldwins Gardens
London EC1N 7RJ
Tel: 0171 831 9831
http://www.vois.org.uk/cf

Depression Alliance
35 Westminster Bridge Road
London SE1 7JB
Tel: 0171 633 9929
http://www.gn.apc.org/da

Disabled Living Foundation
380–384 Harrow Road
London W9 2HU
Tel: 0870 603 9177
http://www.dlf.org.uk

Parkinson's Disease Society
215 Vauxhall Bridge Road
London SW1V 1EJ
Tel: 0171 233 5373
http://www.shef.ac.uk/misc/groups/epda.home.html

The Royal Association for Disability and Rehabilitation (RADAR)
12 City Forum
250 City Road
London EC1V 8AF
Tel: 0171 250 3222
Minicom number (for hard of hearing) 0171 250 4119

Royal National Institute for the Blind
224 Great Portland Street
London W1N 6AA
Tel: 0345 669 999
http://www.rnib.org.uk

Royal National Institute for the Deaf
19–23 Featherstone Street
London EC1Y 8SL
Tel: 0870 605 0123
Minicom number (for those hard of hearing): 0870 603 3007
http://www.rnid.org.uk

Stroke Association
Stroke House
123–127 Whitecross Street
London EC1Y 8JJ
Tel: 0171 566 0300

Further reading

Books

Caring in a crisis: finding and paying for residential and nursing home care, by Marina Lewycka. Age Concern.
ISBN 0 862 42157 8

The Carer's Act (The Carer's Recognition and Services Act 1995).
The Stationery Office. ISBN 0 105412953

Care Homes Directory. Select 1000 Homes Directories.
ISBN 1 898 59712 X. Phone 0122 320 7770 for details or look at web page http://www.careselect.co.uk

A better home life. Centre for Policy on Ageing.
ISBN 0 904 13991 3. Phone 0171 253 1787 for details.

Leaflets

(the addresses for these organisations are listed in the Resources section on pages 63–73).

Age Concern factsheets

10   *Local authority charging procedures for residential and nursing home care*

29   *Finding residential and nursing home accommodation*

32   *Disability and ageing: your rights to social services*

37   *Hospital discharge arrangements and NHS continuing health care services*

Counsel and Care factsheets

Elderly Accommodation Counsel

Choosing the right home

Relatives Association

The Association publishes a number of booklets giving accounts of relatives' views or experiences.